A SURVIVAL GUIDE

for

FRACTIONS
PERCENTAGES
&
DECIMALS

by

Dougie Macfarlane

ISBN 0 7169 0083 1

© D. Macfarlane, 2002.

ROBERT GIBSON · **Publisher**

17 Fitzroy Place, Glasgow, G3 7SF, Scotland, U.K.

www.gibson-books.co.uk

INTRODUCTION

With the arrival of non-calculator papers in Scottish education, pupils are now effectively examined on basic mathematical skills.

Fractions, Percentages and Decimals are often poorly understood.

Calculators are useful but not essential tools and this Survival Guide is designed for use without one.

Knowledge of multiplication tables is essential. These are included at the back, together with a multiplication and division chart.

There are plenty of examples, exercises and summaries, and, at the end of each chapter, a self-evaluation to test if mastery has been achieved.

There is rarely just one way of solving a problem and alternative strategies are suggested throughout the text.

CONTENTS

CHAPTER 1

FRACTIONS

INTRODUCTION TO FRACTIONS

A **fraction** is a **part** of a whole thing divided up into equal parts.

For instance,

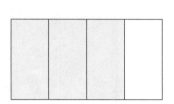 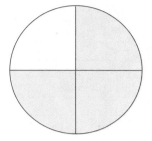 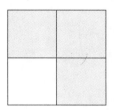

are all represented by the fraction **three quarters** or $\frac{3}{4}$.

The **top number** of the fraction is called the **numerator** and the **bottom number** is called the **denominator**.

Here the numerator (*or the number of parts we're interested in*) is **3** and the denominator (or *the total number of parts the whole has been divided into*) is **4.**

In the case of $\frac{5}{6}$,

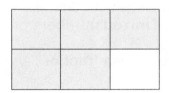

the numerator is 5 and the denominator is 6.

The **fraction line** itself means **divides** or **divided by**, so the first example could read, *3 divided by 4*, and the second, *5 divided by 6*.

Here's a quick summary so far:

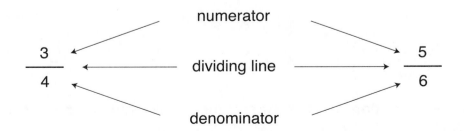

MIXED NUMBERS AND IMPROPER FRACTIONS

A **very special fraction** is one where the **numerator is the same as the denominator** such as:

$$\frac{2}{2}, \frac{3}{3}, \frac{4}{4}, \text{ etc.}$$

Which are of course (as you can see from the diagram) exactly the same as **one** (whole).

Fractions equivalent to **one** are very useful, as we shall soon see.

We usually think of fractions as being less than one, but we can deal with fractions bigger than one too. These are called **mixed numbers** or **improper fractions**.

A **mixed number** is simply a **number plus a fraction**.

Here is $1\frac{1}{2}$, meaning "*one whole (thing) plus half (of it).*"

$2\frac{1}{5}$ is another example of a mixed number.

An **improper fraction** is one where the **numerator is bigger than the denominator**. (*Think of it as a "top heavy" fraction.*)

Here are two examples of improper fractions:

$$\frac{3}{2} \text{ and } \frac{11}{5}$$

Mixed numbers and improper fractions are in fact the **same thing** and we can change from one to the other very easily. Let's go from mixed numbers to improper fractions first.

EXAMPLE

Change $2\frac{1}{2}$ to an improper fraction.

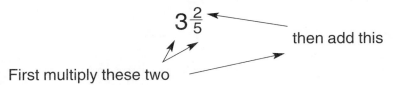

$2\frac{1}{2}$ and then add the numerator $(4 + 1 = 5)$

First multiply these two together $(2 \times 2 = 4)$.

This new result (5) goes over the old denominator (2):

$$2\frac{1}{2} = \frac{(2 \times 2) + 1}{2}$$

$$= \frac{5}{2}$$

Here's another example of changing a **mixed number** to an **improper fraction**:

$3\frac{2}{5}$ then add this

First multiply these two

and the result goes over 5, like this:

$$3\frac{2}{5} = \frac{(3 \times 5) + 2}{5}$$

$$= \frac{15 + 2}{5}$$

$$= \frac{17}{5}$$

Easy isn't it? Now here's some for you to try:

Exercise 1.1   *(The answers are on page 11.)*

Change these mixed numbers to improper fractions:

(a) $1\frac{5}{8}$ *(b)* $1\frac{3}{4}$ *(c)* $2\frac{1}{3}$ *(d)* $2\frac{1}{7}$

(e) $7\frac{1}{2}$ *(f)* $9\frac{2}{5}$ *(g)* $10\frac{2}{7}$ *(h)* $12\frac{2}{3}$

Now let's go from an **improper fraction** to a **mixed number**.

This time we **divide the bottom into the top and write the remainder as a fraction**.

Like this:

EXAMPLE

Change $\frac{33}{4}$ into a mixed number.

$$\frac{33}{4}$$

Divide the denominator (bottom)

into the numerator (top)

and write the **remainder**

as a **fraction**

We get **8** remainder **1**. (*Remember:* $8 \times 4 = 32$)

So here's the answer:

Result of the division $8\frac{1}{4}$ ⟵ Remainder

⟵ Original denominator

Watch it being done again:

EXAMPLE

Write $\frac{35}{6}$ as a mixed number.

As before, we divide bottom (6) into top (35) and write the remainder as a fraction:

Remainder

$5\frac{5}{6}$ (*Remember:* $5 \times 6 = 30$)

And now some for you to try.

Exercise 1.2   *(The answers are given on page 11.)*

Change these improper fractions to mixed numbers:

(a) $\frac{16}{3}$ (b) $\frac{21}{4}$ (c) $\frac{23}{5}$ (d) $\frac{37}{7}$

(e) $\frac{51}{8}$ (f) $\frac{20}{19}$ (g) $\frac{45}{22}$ (h) $\frac{100}{97}$

SUMMARY

♦   Fractions are **parts of a whole**.

♦   The top part of the fraction is called the **numerator**.

♦   The bottom part of a fraction is called the **denominator**.

♦   The line in a fraction means **divides**.

♦   A special fraction is when the **numerator equals the denominator** and is the same as **one**.

♦   An **improper** fraction has the **numerator bigger than the denominator**.

♦   A **mixed number** can be changed into an **improper** fraction by **multiplying** and **adding**.

♦   An **improper fraction** can be changed into a **mixed number** by **dividing** the denominator into the numerator and writing the **remainder as a fraction**.

ANSWERS

Exercise 1.1

(a) $\dfrac{13}{8}$ (b) $\dfrac{7}{4}$ (c) $\dfrac{7}{3}$ (d) $\dfrac{15}{7}$ (e) $\dfrac{15}{2}$ (f) $\dfrac{47}{5}$ (g) $\dfrac{72}{7}$ (h) $\dfrac{38}{3}$

Exercise 1.2

(a) $5\dfrac{1}{3}$ (b) $5\dfrac{1}{4}$ (c) $4\dfrac{3}{5}$ (d) $5\dfrac{2}{7}$ (e) $6\dfrac{3}{8}$ (f) $1\dfrac{1}{19}$

(g) $2\dfrac{1}{22}$ (h) $1\dfrac{3}{97}$

MULTIPLYING FRACTIONS

Have you understood everything so far? If not, go back and look at it again or, better still, get someone to help you.

If the problem is with tables, there are no short cuts! You know what you have to do!

The next thing we look at is **multiplying fractions** which is **easy**!

You just **multiply the numerators together and the denominators together**.

Like this,

$$\frac{2}{3} \times \frac{4}{5} = \frac{8}{15}$$

or like this.

$$\frac{2}{7} \times \frac{3}{5} = \frac{6}{35}$$

If the result is an **improper fraction**, always give your answer as a **mixed number**.

$$\frac{5}{3} \times \frac{4}{3} = \frac{20}{9}$$

$$= 2\frac{2}{9}$$

It couldn't be easier could it?

Now it's your turn.

Exercise 1.3 *(The answers are given on page 21.)*

Multiply these pairs of fractions together:

(a) $\frac{1}{2}$ and $\frac{1}{3}$ (b) $\frac{2}{5}$ and $\frac{1}{7}$ (c) $\frac{3}{8}$ and $\frac{1}{4}$

(d) $\frac{1}{5}$ and $\frac{1}{9}$ (e) $\frac{5}{7}$ and $\frac{1}{8}$ (f) $\frac{5}{8}$ and $\frac{5}{9}$

CANCELLING FRACTIONS

Very often it is possible to **simplify** fractions. This is often called **cancelling**, or sometimes **cancelling down**. These pictures tell part of the story:

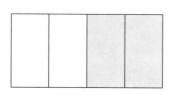

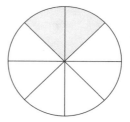

$$\frac{2}{4} = \frac{1}{2}$$

$$\frac{2}{8} = \frac{1}{4}$$

We can see why these fraction are equal from the diagrams, but we know it to be true from **something else we've already learnt**.

Look at this:

$$\frac{2}{4} = \frac{2 \times 1}{2 \times 2}$$

$$= \left(\frac{2}{2}\right) \times \frac{1}{2}$$

But $\frac{2}{2}$ is the same as **ONE**, and **ANYTHING** multiplied by **ONE** is **ITSELF**.

$$= 1 \times \frac{1}{2}$$

$$= \frac{1}{2}$$

So $\frac{2}{4}$ is the same as $\frac{1}{2}$.

We say that $\frac{2}{4}$ **cancels down to** $\frac{1}{2}$. In other words, $\frac{2}{4}$ and $\frac{1}{2}$ are identical (**equivalent**) fractions (but $\frac{1}{2}$ is the simplest version).

Similarly,

$$\frac{2}{8} = \frac{2 \times 1}{2 \times 4}$$

$$= \left(\frac{2}{2}\right) \times \frac{1}{4}$$

$$= 1 \times \frac{1}{4}$$

$$= \frac{1}{4}$$

So $\frac{2}{8}$ is the same as $\frac{1}{4}$.

Something to think about:

We can of course go **the other way**, that is, take a simple fraction and make it more 'complicated' just by multiplying it by a new fraction equivalent to **one**.

Here's an example:

$$\frac{2}{3} = \frac{2}{3} \times 1$$

$$= \frac{2}{3} \times \frac{8}{8}$$

$$= \frac{2 \times 8}{3 \times 8}$$

$$= \frac{16}{24}$$

We will meet this important idea again soon. In the meantime, here are some more examples of **cancellation**.

EXAMPLE

Cancel the fraction $\frac{9}{15}$ down to its simplest form.

$$\frac{9}{15} = \frac{3 \times 3}{3 \times 5}$$

$$= \left(\frac{3}{3}\right) \times \frac{3}{5}$$

$$= 1 \times \frac{3}{5}$$

$$= \frac{3}{5}$$

So $\frac{9}{15}$ is the same as $\frac{3}{5}$.

We always need to be sure that we *have* in fact arrived at the simplest answer as this next example shows.

EXAMPLE

Cancel the fraction $\frac{18}{24}$ down to its simplest form.

$$\frac{18}{24} = \frac{3 \times 6}{3 \times 8}$$

$$= \left(\frac{3}{3}\right) \times \frac{6}{8}$$

$$= 1 \times \frac{6}{8}$$

$$= \frac{6}{8}$$

*It looks like we've got the answer, but we haven't. Notice that **TWO** will divide exactly into both six and eight. So we go on.*

$$= \frac{2 \times 3}{2 \times 4}$$

$$= \left(\frac{2}{2}\right) \times \frac{3}{4}$$

$$= 1 \times \frac{3}{4}$$

$$= \frac{3}{4}$$

$\frac{18}{24}$ is equivalent to $\frac{3}{4}$

The process of cancellation is often taught by the teacher explaining the process verbally.

When written down, it is sometimes not clear what is actually going on.

You've maybe seen it written like this:

$$\frac{\cancel{18}^{\,6}}{\cancel{24}_{\,8}}$$

Here is the explanation that goes with it.

> The eighteen is scored out and is replaced by a six, meaning that **three** (unwritten) divides into eighteen exactly six times.

> Likewise, the twenty-four is scored out and replaced by an eight, meaning that **three** (again unwritten) divides into twenty-four exactly eight times.

And by the same reasoning (this time using an unwritten **two**):

$$\frac{\cancel{6}^{\,3}}{\cancel{8}_{\,4}}$$

So $\frac{18}{24}$ is the same as (cancels down to) $\frac{3}{4}$.

You might have noticed that $\frac{18}{24}$ can be written as $\frac{3 \times 6}{4 \times 6}$

$$= \frac{3}{4} \times \frac{6}{6}$$

$$= \frac{3}{4} \times 1$$

$$= \frac{3}{4}$$

and you would have got the right answer much quicker. It doesn't matter how long it takes. The important thing is to make sure that your final answer cannot be cancelled down.

Got the idea?

Now you can try some.

Exercise 1.4   (The answers are given on page 21.)

Cancel these fractions down to their simplest form.

(a) $\dfrac{2}{6}$ (b) $\dfrac{9}{12}$ (c) $\dfrac{10}{16}$ (d) $\dfrac{15}{24}$

(e) $\dfrac{3}{21}$ (f) $\dfrac{15}{25}$ (g) $\dfrac{95}{100}$ (h) $\dfrac{24}{36}$

Cancellation can also be done when fractions are being multiplied.

EXAMPLE

Simplify $\frac{3}{5} \times \frac{10}{9}$.

$$\frac{3}{5} \times \frac{10}{9}$$

$$= \frac{3 \times 10}{5 \times 9}$$

$$= \frac{3 \times 5 \times 2}{5 \times 3 \times 3}$$

$$= \frac{3 \times 5 \times 2}{3 \times 5 \times 3}$$

Remember: It's OK to rearrange multiplication:
$$(3 \times 2 = 2 \times 3)$$

$$= \left(\frac{3}{3}\right) \times \left(\frac{5}{5}\right) \times \left(\frac{2}{3}\right)$$

$$= 1 \times 1 \times \left(\frac{2}{3}\right)$$

$$= \left(\frac{2}{3}\right)$$

$\frac{3}{5} \times \frac{10}{9} = \frac{2}{3}$ in its simplest form.

This is usually seen written as

$$\overset{1}{\cancel{\frac{3}{5}}} \times \overset{2}{\cancel{\frac{10}{9}}}$$
$$\underset{1}{} \quad \underset{3}{}$$

We can of course multiply **more than two** fractions together at one time and the next example shows this together with an important idea often overlooked or misunderstood.

EXAMPLE

Simplify $\frac{2}{7} \times \frac{3}{12} \times \frac{14}{4}$.

$$\frac{2}{7} \times \frac{3}{12} \times \frac{14}{4} = \frac{2 \times 3 \times 7 \times 2}{7 \times 3 \times 4 \times 4}$$

$$= \frac{2 \times 2 \times 3 \times 7 \times 1}{2 \times 2 \times 3 \times 7 \times 2 \times 2} \longleftarrow \text{Note the unwritten "one"}$$

$$= \left(\frac{2}{2}\right) \times \left(\frac{2}{2}\right) \times \left(\frac{3}{3}\right) \times \left(\frac{7}{7}\right) \times \left(\frac{1}{2 \times 2}\right)$$

$$= \frac{1}{4} \longleftarrow \textbf{Not zero} *$$

Now it's over to you again.

Exercise 1.5   *(The answers are given on page 21.)*

Simplify.

(a) $\frac{1}{4} \times \frac{6}{5}$

(b) $\frac{4}{3} \times \frac{2}{8}$

(c) $\frac{1}{9} \times \frac{12}{1}$

(d) $\frac{3}{12} \times \frac{4}{6}$

(e) $\frac{14}{7} \times \frac{2}{4}$

(f) $\frac{9}{21} \times \frac{14}{6}$

(g) $\frac{3}{2} \times \frac{15}{9} \times \frac{2}{5}$

(h) $\frac{2}{9} \times \frac{7}{14} \times \frac{16}{4}$

---

* Cancelling is nothing to do with 'making things disappear'. When all the numbers have 'gone' from the top line, it is **one** that is left, not 'nothing'. This is a common error.

SUMMARY

♦ Multiplying fractions is **easy**. **Multiply the numerators together and the denominators together**.

♦ If the answer is an improper fraction, change it to a mixed number.

♦ If the numerator and denominator are made up of numbers which are the same top and bottom, i.e., equivalent to **one**, then we can simplify or **cancel down** the fraction.

♦ This cancellation can be done when fractions are being multiplied.

ANSWERS

Exercise 1.3

(a) $\frac{1}{6}$ (b) $\frac{2}{35}$ (c) $\frac{3}{32}$ (d) $\frac{1}{45}$ (e) $\frac{5}{56}$ (f) $\frac{25}{72}$

Exercise 1.4

(a) $\frac{1}{3}$ (b) $\frac{3}{4}$ (c) $\frac{5}{8}$ (d) $\frac{5}{8}$ (e) $\frac{1}{7}$ (f) $\frac{3}{5}$ (g) $\frac{19}{20}$ (h) $\frac{2}{3}$

Exercise 1.5

(a) $\frac{3}{10}$ (b) $\frac{1}{3}$ (c) $1\frac{1}{3}$ (d) $\frac{1}{6}$ (e) 1   (f) 1   (g) 1   (h) $\frac{4}{9}$

COMPARING FRACTIONS

We all know that 5 is bigger than 2 and we can easily see from the diagram that $\frac{5}{6}$ is bigger than $\frac{2}{6}$.

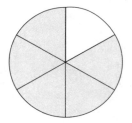 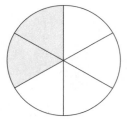

But which is the biggest between $\frac{5}{7}$ and $\frac{2}{3}$?

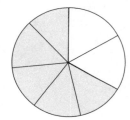 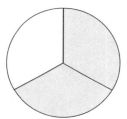

Not so easy to see now, is it?

COMMON DENOMINATORS

We can only compare fractions when they have the **same denominator**. (Fractions with the same denominator are said to have **common denominators**.) Once we have that, **the fraction with the biggest numerator is the biggest fraction**.

How do we change them so that the denominators are the same?

Easy! We multiply them both by a fraction equal to one (which of course doesn't really change them at all)! Remember: **The new fractions formed in this way are equivalent to the original ones**. Their **appearance** has changed but their **value** has not.

Watch this:

$$\frac{5}{7} = \frac{5}{7} \times 1$$

$$= \frac{5}{7} \times \left(\frac{3}{3}\right) \qquad \text{Why choose } \left(\frac{3}{3}\right)? \text{ Why not } \left(\frac{2}{2}\right) \text{ or } \left(\frac{5}{5}\right)?$$

$$= \frac{5 \times 3}{7 \times 3}$$

$$= \frac{15}{21}$$

So $\frac{5}{7}$ is exactly the same as the fraction $\frac{15}{21}$.

"So what?" You may well ask. *Indeed . . . read on*.

$$\frac{2}{3} = \frac{2}{3} \times 1$$

$$= \frac{2}{3} \times \left(\frac{7}{7}\right) \qquad \text{Why } \left(\frac{7}{7}\right)???$$

$$= \frac{2 \times 7}{3 \times 7}$$

$$= \frac{14}{21}$$

So $\frac{2}{3}$ is the same as $\frac{14}{21}$ and $\frac{5}{7}$ is the same as $\frac{15}{21}$.

One look at the numerators will tell you that $\frac{5}{7}$ is bigger than $\frac{2}{3}$!

Let's look at this technique again.

EXAMPLE

Which fraction is bigger $\frac{3}{5}$ and $\frac{5}{9}$?

$\frac{3}{5} = \frac{3}{5} \times \left(\frac{9}{9}\right) = \frac{27}{45}$ Can you now see why we used $\frac{9}{9}$?

$\frac{5}{9} = \frac{5}{9} \times \left(\frac{5}{5}\right) = \frac{25}{45}$ Can you now see why we used $\frac{5}{5}$?

From the new numerators, $\frac{3}{5}$ is bigger than $\frac{5}{9}$.

What is happening is like this:

$$\left(\frac{9}{9}\right) \times \frac{3}{5} \qquad \frac{5}{9} \times \left(\frac{5}{5}\right)$$

Easy isn't it?

Your turn.

Exercise 1.6   *(The answers are given on page 29.)*

Which is the bigger in each of these pairs of fractions?

(a) $\frac{1}{2}$ or $\frac{4}{9}$?   *(b)* $\frac{1}{3}$ or $\frac{2}{7}$?   *(c)* $\frac{3}{5}$ or $\frac{2}{7}$?

(d) $\frac{3}{4}$ or $\frac{7}{9}$?   *(e)* $\frac{5}{8}$ or $\frac{7}{9}$?   *(f)* $\frac{5}{8}$ or $\frac{4}{9}$?

ADDING FRACTIONS 1

As we have just seen, fractions can only be compared when they have common denominators.

This is also the case with addition.

Fractions can be added **only if the denominators are the same**.

Like this:

$$\frac{1}{5} + \frac{3}{5} = \frac{1+3}{5} \qquad\qquad \text{or} \qquad\qquad \frac{4}{7} + \frac{5}{7} = \frac{4+5}{7}$$

$$= \frac{4}{5} \qquad\qquad\qquad\qquad\qquad = \frac{9}{7}$$

$$\qquad\qquad\qquad\qquad\qquad\qquad\qquad\qquad = 1\frac{2}{7}$$

Now consider $\frac{1}{3}$ and $\frac{1}{2}$. These fractions can **not** be added in this way because the denominators are different.

This is definitely **wrong**!

$$\frac{1}{3} + \frac{1}{2} = \frac{1+1}{2+3} = \frac{2}{5} \quad \textbf{X !}$$

What we must do first is **change the denominators** using the same technique we have just seen used to **compare fractions**. In other words, **we need to form new equivalent fractions which have common denominators**. Only then can the fractions be added.

Here it is being done:

$$\frac{1}{3} + \frac{1}{2} = \frac{1}{3} \times \left(\frac{2}{2}\right) + \frac{1}{2} \times \left(\frac{3}{3}\right)$$

$$= \frac{1 \times 2}{6} + \frac{1 \times 3}{6}$$

$$= \frac{2}{6} + \frac{3}{6} \qquad\qquad \text{[\textbf{Now} the fractions can be added.]}$$

$$= \frac{5}{6}$$

Sometimes, we only need to deal with **one** fraction in order to get both denominators the same.

$$\frac{3}{4} + \frac{1}{2} = \frac{3}{4} + \frac{1}{2} \times \left(\frac{2}{2}\right)$$

$$= \frac{3}{4} + \frac{1 \times 2}{2 \times 2}$$

$$= \frac{3}{4} + \frac{2}{4}$$

$$= \frac{3+2}{4} = \frac{5}{4}$$

$$= 1\frac{1}{4}$$

In the first example, 3 and 2 were the original denominators. 6 is a **common denominator** meaning that **both 2 and 3 will divide into 6 with no remainder**.

Of course, 2 and 3 will also divide exactly into 12 (and 24), but we always use the smallest or **lowest common denominator** sometimes abbreviated as **LCD**.

In the second example, 4 is the LCD of 2 and 4 so the fraction $\frac{3}{4}$ did not need to be changed.

Now some practice in finding lowest common denominators:

Exercise 1.7   *(The answers are given on page 29.)*

Find the LCD between these denominators. *

(a)   3 and 9   *(b)*   2 and 6   *(c)*   3 and 4

(d)   5 and 7   *(e)*   8 and 10   *(f)*   2, 3 and 4

  * ***Hint:*** You can always find a common denominator by multiplying the numbers together, but it is not always the LCD. Check your answer by dividing it by one of the numbers. Is the answer still a common denominator?

EXAMPLE

$$\frac{1}{8} + \frac{1}{4} = \frac{1}{8} + \frac{1}{4} \times \left(\frac{2}{2}\right) \qquad \text{LCD} = 8$$

$$= \frac{1}{8} + \frac{1 \times 2}{4 \times 2}$$

$$= \frac{1}{8} + \frac{2}{8}$$

$$= \frac{1 + 2}{8}$$

$$= \frac{3}{8} \qquad \text{CHECK: Is this an improper fraction or will it cancel down? No.}$$

EXAMPLE

$$\frac{2}{3} + \frac{1}{4} = \frac{2}{3} \times \left(\frac{4}{4}\right) + \frac{1}{4} \times \left(\frac{3}{3}\right) \qquad \text{LCD} = 12$$

$$= \frac{2 \times 4}{3 \times 4} + \frac{1 \times 3}{4 \times 3}$$

$$= \frac{8}{12} + \frac{3}{12}$$

$$= \frac{8 + 3}{12}$$

$$= \frac{11}{12} \qquad \text{CHECK: Is this an improper fraction or will it cancel down? No.}$$

Exercise 1.8   *(The answers are given on page 29.)*

Add these fractions together.

(a) $\frac{1}{2} + \frac{1}{8}$ *(b)* $\frac{2}{9} + \frac{2}{3}$ *(c)* $\frac{3}{5} + \frac{1}{10}$

(d) $\frac{1}{3} + \frac{1}{4}$ *(e)* $\frac{2}{5} + \frac{1}{6}$ *(f)* $\frac{2}{7} + \frac{1}{8}$

SUMMARY

♦ Fractions can be changed by multiplying them by a **new fraction** equivalent to **one**. *(Which of course doesn't really change them at all!)* The new fraction is equivalent to the original. The **appearance** has changed but the **value** has not.

♦ We can only compare the **sizes** of fractions if they have the **same denominators**.

♦ Similarly, fractions can only be **added** when they have the **same** denominators.

♦ We use **exactly the same technique to change one or both of the fractions so that they can be compared or added**.

♦ The **Least Common Denominator** (LCD) is the best choice when adding fractions (although any common denominator will do). It is always wise to check that the **final answer is not an improper fraction and cannot be cancelled down**.

ANSWERS

Exercise 1.6

(a) $\dfrac{1}{2}$ (b) $\dfrac{1}{3}$ (c) $\dfrac{3}{5}$ (d) $\dfrac{7}{9}$ (e) $\dfrac{7}{9}$ (f) $\dfrac{5}{8}$

Exercise 1.7

(a) 9   (b) 6   (c) 12   (d) 35   (e) 40   (f) 12

Exercise 1.8

(a) $\dfrac{5}{8}$ (b) $\dfrac{8}{9}$ (c) $\dfrac{7}{10}$ (d) $\dfrac{7}{12}$ (e) $\dfrac{17}{30}$ (f) $\dfrac{23}{56}$

ADDING FRACTIONS 2

If you have understood everything so far, congratulations! You are well on the way to completely understanding fractions. However, learning anything properly takes practice so here's some more addition of fractions and some subtractions as well.

EXAMPLE 1

Add: $1\frac{1}{3} + 1\frac{1}{5}$

Immediately, this **looks** different . . . but it's **easy**!

Just change both mixed numbers to **improper** fractions and proceed as before.

$$1\frac{1}{3} + 1\frac{1}{5} = \frac{4}{3} + \frac{6}{5} \qquad \text{LCD} = 5 \times 3 = 15$$

$$= \frac{4}{3} \times \left(\frac{5}{5}\right) + \frac{6}{5} \times \left(\frac{3}{3}\right)$$

$$= \frac{4 \times 5}{3 \times 5} + \frac{6 \times 3}{5 \times 3}$$

$$= \frac{20}{15} + \frac{18}{15}$$

$$= \frac{20 + 18}{15}$$

$$= \frac{38}{15} \qquad \text{Change this to a mixed number}$$

$$= 2\frac{8}{15} \qquad \textbf{Note}: \ 2 \times 15 = 30$$
$$\text{Cancel down? No.}$$

So, $1\frac{1}{3} + 1\frac{1}{5} = 2\frac{8}{15}$

Never leave an improper fraction as your answer and always check that nothing can be cancelled down.

Here's another:

EXAMPLE 2

Add: $2\frac{1}{2} + 1\frac{1}{3}$

$$2\frac{1}{2} + 1\frac{1}{3} = \frac{5}{2} + \frac{4}{3}$$

$$\text{LCD} = 2 \times 3 = 6$$

$$= \frac{5}{2} \times \left(\frac{3}{3}\right) + \frac{4}{3} \times \left(\frac{2}{2}\right)$$

$$= \frac{15}{6} + \frac{8}{6}$$

$$= \frac{15 + 8}{6}$$

$$= \frac{23}{6}$$

$$= 3\frac{5}{6} \qquad (3 \times 6 = 18; \quad 18 + 5 = 23)$$

Now it's your turn.

Exercise 1.9   *(The answers are given on page 35.)*

Add the following.

(a) $1\frac{1}{4} + \frac{1}{8}$ (b) $\frac{1}{10} + 1\frac{1}{5}$ (c) $3\frac{1}{9} + 1\frac{1}{3}$

(d) $1\frac{1}{5} + 1\frac{1}{2}$ (e) $1\frac{1}{4} + 1\frac{1}{3}$ (f) $2\frac{2}{5} + 1\frac{2}{3}$

SUBTRACTING FRACTIONS

Subtracting fractions is (you guessed it) **easy!** We do it in **exactly the same way as adding fractions**. (Except, of course, we subtract instead of add!)

Here are two examples.

EXAMPLE 1

Simplify: $\dfrac{5}{6} - \dfrac{1}{3}$

$$\dfrac{5}{6} - \dfrac{1}{3} = \dfrac{5}{6} - \dfrac{1}{3} \times \left(\dfrac{2}{2}\right) \qquad\qquad \text{LCD} = 6$$

$$= \dfrac{5}{6} - \left(\dfrac{1 \times 2}{3 \times 2}\right)$$

$$= \dfrac{5}{6} - \dfrac{2}{6}$$

$$= \dfrac{5 - 2}{6}$$

$$= \dfrac{3}{6} \qquad\qquad \text{Cancel down? Yes!}$$

$$= \dfrac{3 \times 1}{3 \times 2}$$

$$= 1 \times \dfrac{1}{2}$$

$$= \dfrac{1}{2}$$

So: $\dfrac{5}{6} - \dfrac{1}{3} = \dfrac{1}{2}$

EXAMPLE 2

Simplify: $2\frac{1}{3} - 1\frac{1}{4}$

$$2\frac{1}{3} - 1\frac{1}{4} = \frac{7}{3} - \frac{5}{4}$$

$$= \frac{7}{3} \times \left(\frac{4}{4}\right) - \frac{5}{4} \times \left(\frac{3}{3}\right)$$

$$= \frac{28}{12} - \frac{15}{12}$$

$$= \frac{13}{12}$$

$$= 1\frac{1}{12}$$

So: $2\frac{1}{3} - 1\frac{1}{4} = 1\frac{1}{12}$

Your turn.

Exercise 1.10   *(The answers are given on page 35.)*

(a) $1\frac{1}{4} - \frac{1}{8}$ *(b)* $1\frac{1}{5} - \frac{1}{10}$ *(c)* $3\frac{1}{9} - 1\frac{1}{3}$

(d) $1\frac{1}{2} - 1\frac{1}{3}$ *(e)* $5\frac{1}{4} - 2\frac{1}{5}$ *(f)* $3\frac{1}{9} - 1\frac{1}{4}$

SUMMARY

♦ **Subtracting** fractions is exactly the same as **adding** them . . . except of course, you subtract!

♦ If the question involves **mixed numbers**, turn them into **improper fractions** and proceed as before.

♦ **Never leave your answer as an improper fraction** . . . turn it into a **mixed number** and lastly,

♦ Always check that your **final answer cannot be cancelled down**.

ANSWERS

Exercise 1.9

(a) $1\frac{3}{8}$ (b) $1\frac{3}{10}$ (c) $4\frac{4}{9}$ (d) $2\frac{7}{10}$ (e) $2\frac{7}{12}$ (f) $4\frac{1}{15}$

Exercise 1.10

(a) $1\frac{1}{8}$ (b) $1\frac{1}{10}$ (c) $1\frac{7}{9}$ (d) $\frac{1}{6}$ (e) $3\frac{1}{20}$ (f) $1\frac{31}{36}$

FINDING A FRACTIONAL PART OF A NUMBER

What about finding a fractional part of some whole number? Typical problems might be the following examples.

EXAMPLE 1

Find $\frac{5}{8}$ of 200.

But first, did you know that **any number can be written as itself over one**?

Well, you do now! So 200 can be written as $\frac{200}{1}$.

Second, in maths, the word **of** means **multiplied by**.

Put these facts together and the problem simplifies to the **multiplication of two fractions**.

$$\frac{5}{8} \text{ of } 200 = \frac{5}{8} \times \frac{200}{1}$$

$$= \frac{5 \times 200}{8 \times 1}$$

$$= \frac{1000}{8}$$

$$= 125 \qquad 1000 \div 8 = 125. \qquad \text{So } \frac{5}{8} \text{ of } 200 = 125.$$

Here's another:

EXAMPLE 2

Find $\frac{5}{6}$ of 200.

$$\frac{5}{6} \text{ of } 200 = \frac{5}{6} \times \frac{200}{1}$$

$$= \frac{5 \times 200}{6 \times 1}$$

$$= \frac{1000}{6} \qquad \text{Change this to a mixed number.}$$

$$= 166\frac{4}{6} \qquad \text{Cancel down.}$$

$$= 166\frac{2}{3}$$

Find

(a) $\frac{2}{3}$ of 3000

(b) $\frac{5}{6}$ of 120

(c) $\frac{3}{4}$ of 720

(d) $\frac{2}{5}$ of 1100

(e) $\frac{9}{10}$ of 412

(f) $\frac{4}{5}$ of 1121

So far, we have dealt with multiplying fractions, adding them and subtracting them. That leaves only the **division of fractions** which is . . . **easy!**

DIVISION OF FRACTIONS

EXAMPLE 1

What is $\frac{1}{2} \div \frac{1}{3}$?

The rules for the division of fractions are:

1.   Leave the first fraction as it is.

2.   Change the ÷ sign to ×.

3.   Turn the second fraction upside down.

4.   Multiply as normal.

And here is how it's done:

$$\frac{1}{2} \div \frac{1}{3} = \frac{1}{2} \times \frac{3}{1}$$

$$= \frac{1 \times 3}{2 \times 1}$$

$$= \frac{3}{2}$$

$$= 1\frac{1}{2}$$

EXAMPLE 2

$3\frac{1}{5} \div 2\frac{1}{4}$

Just change the mixed numbers to improper fractions and proceed as normal.

$$= \frac{16}{5} \div \frac{9}{4}$$

$$= \frac{16}{5} \times \frac{4}{9}$$

$$= \frac{16 \times 4}{5 \times 9}$$

$$= \frac{64}{45} \quad \text{Change to a mixed number}$$

$$= 1\frac{20}{45} \quad \text{and don't forget to cancel down!}$$

$$= 1\frac{5 \times 4}{5 \times 9}$$

$$= 1\frac{4}{9}$$

Now over to you.

Exercise 1.12   *(The answers are given on page 42.)*

Find

(a) $\frac{2}{3} \div \frac{3}{4}$

(b) $\frac{4}{3} \div \frac{3}{2}$

(c) $\frac{3}{4} \div 4$

(d) $4 \div \frac{4}{3}$

(e) $1\frac{1}{4} \div \frac{1}{2}$

(f) $2\frac{1}{4} \div 1\frac{1}{2}$

And finally something that looks **really weird**!

EXAMPLE 3

Simplify $\dfrac{\frac{2}{3}}{\frac{5}{6}}$

Yes it **does** make sense if you remember that the fraction line means 'divides', so this problem is really $\dfrac{2}{3} \div \dfrac{5}{6}$.

No problem.

$$\frac{2}{3} \div \frac{5}{6} = \frac{2}{3} \times \frac{6}{5}$$

$$= \frac{2 \times 6}{3 \times 5}$$

$$= \frac{12}{15}$$

$$= \frac{3 \times 4}{3 \times 5}$$

$$= \frac{4}{5}$$

The example we have just seen shows a different way of expressing the division of fractions.

It also leads to an explanation of **why** the rules for division work.

We already know from our first example that

$$\frac{1}{2} \div \frac{1}{3} = \frac{1}{2} \times \frac{3}{1} = \frac{3}{2} = 1\frac{1}{2} \quad \text{(according to the rules).}$$

Watch it being done again in detail and see if you can follow the argument line by line:

$$\frac{1}{2} \div \frac{1}{3} = \frac{\frac{1}{2}}{\frac{1}{3}} \quad \text{From } \textbf{EXAMPLE 3}$$

$$= \frac{\frac{1}{2}}{\frac{1}{3}} \times 1$$

$$= \frac{\frac{1}{2}}{\frac{1}{3}} \times \frac{3}{3} \qquad \left(\frac{3}{3} = 1\right)$$

$$= \frac{\frac{1}{2}}{\frac{1}{3}} \times \frac{\frac{3}{1}}{\frac{3}{1}} \qquad \left(3 = \frac{3}{1}\right)$$

$$= \frac{\frac{1 \times 3}{2 \times 1}}{\frac{1 \times 3}{3 \times 1}} \qquad \text{(Rules for multiplying fractions.)}$$

$$= \frac{\frac{3}{2}}{\frac{3}{3}}$$

$$= \frac{\frac{3}{2}}{1} \qquad \left(\frac{3}{3} = 1\right)$$

$$= \frac{3}{2}$$

$$= 1\frac{1}{2}$$

This is the answer the rules told us to expect.

Congratulations if you were able to follow all of that. You will **not** be asked to repeat it in an examination. What you **will** be expected to do is divide one fraction by another which is really a matter of applying four simple rules.

SUMMARY

♦ Any number can be written as **itself over** (divided by) **one**.

♦ **Of** in mathematics translates as **multiplied by**.

♦ Finding a fractional part of a number is the same as **multiplying fractions**.

♦ The rules for dividing fractions are:

1. The first fraction stays the same.

2. ÷ becomes ×.

3. The second fraction is turned upside down.

4. Multiplication is carried out as usual.

♦ And finally, $\dfrac{\frac{2}{3}}{\frac{5}{6}}$ makes sense if you remember that the fraction line means 'divides'.

ANSWERS

Exercise 1.11

(a) 2000   (b) 100   (c) 540   (d) 440   (e) $370\frac{4}{5}$ (f) $896\frac{4}{5}$

Exercise 1.12

(a) $\frac{8}{9}$ (b) $\frac{8}{9}$ (c) $\frac{3}{16}$ (d) 3   (e) $2\frac{1}{2}$ (f) $1\frac{1}{2}$

TEST ON FRACTIONS

It is important for you to know how much you've learnt. The only way to find out is to test yourself. Here are ten questions worth twenty-five marks. The answers are on the following page so that you will be able to tell immediately how well you have mastered **fractions**.

1. Choose from one of these statements to complete the sentences below:

    bottom number / an improper fraction / a mixed number / 'divides' / top number / one. **(1 mark each)**

    (a) $\frac{3}{3}$ is the same as ....

    (b) $\frac{4}{3}$ is an example of ....

    (c) In a fraction, the denominator is the ....

    (d) The fraction line means ....

    (e) The numerator of a fraction is ....

2. (a) Change this mixed number to an improper fraction: $2\frac{1}{8}$ **1 mark**

    (b) Change this improper fraction to a mixed number: $\frac{33}{6}$ **1 mark**

3. Multiply   (a) $\frac{2}{3}$ by $\frac{1}{5}$ (b) $\frac{5}{3}$ by $\frac{2}{3}$ **(1 mark each)**

4. Cancel these fractions: (a) $\frac{4}{24}$ (b) $\frac{27}{72}$ **(1 mark each)**

5. Simplify: $\frac{12}{6} \times \frac{3}{4}$ **2 marks**

6. Add: $\frac{1}{5} + \frac{1}{4}$ **2 marks**

7. Add: $1\frac{1}{5} + 1\frac{1}{3}$ **2 marks**

8. Simplify: $2\frac{1}{4} - 1\frac{1}{5}$ **2 marks**

9. Find $\frac{2}{3}$ of 390   **2 marks**

10. What is   (a) $\frac{1}{5} \div \frac{1}{4}$?   (b) $1\frac{1}{5} \div 1\frac{1}{4}$?   **(2 marks each)**

Total marks (25)

ANSWERS TO TEST ON FRACTIONS

1. *(a)* one *(b)* improper fraction *(c)* bottom number
   (d) 'divides' *(e)* top number **5 (1 each)**

2. *(a)* $\frac{17}{8}$ *(b)* $5\frac{1}{2}$ **(1 each)**

3. *(a)* $\frac{2}{15}$ *(b)* $1\frac{1}{9}$ **(1 each)**

4. *(a)* $\frac{1}{6}$ *(b)* $\frac{3}{8}$ **(1 each)**

5. $1\frac{1}{2}$ **(2)** 6. $\frac{9}{20}$ **(2)** 7. $2\frac{8}{15}$ **(2)**

8. $2\frac{1}{20}$ **(2)** 9. 260 **(2)**

10. *(a)* $\frac{4}{5}$ **(2)** *(b)* $\frac{24}{25}$ **(2)**

Total marks (25)

INTERPRETING YOUR SCORE

Less than 12 You still have not grasped the fundamentals of fractions. You need more help.

12 to 17 The basics are there but more practice is needed on the weak areas.

18 to 22 A good understanding of the subject which should see you through.

23+ Well done! You have mastered fractions.

CHAPTER 2

PERCENTAGES

FRACTIONS TO PERCENTAGES

Per centum in Latin means 'for every (out of) one hundred'.

A **percentage** is a special type of fraction. It always has **100 as the denominator**.

$$50\% = \frac{50}{100} \qquad\qquad 85\% = \frac{85}{100}$$

Before we explore percentages further, it is useful to remember four important ideas about **fractions**.

---

1. Any number can be written as a fraction — **itself over (divided by) one**, e.g., $3 = \frac{3}{1}$

2. Any fraction that has the same numerator as denominator is the same as **one**, e.g., $\frac{3}{3} = 1$

3. **Multiplying fractions is easy:**
   (numerators × numerators) ÷ (denominators × denominators),
   e.g., $\frac{2}{3} \times \frac{4}{5} = \frac{2 \times 4}{3 \times 5}$

4. Fractions can be changed into (new) **equivalent fractions by multiplying in a fraction equivalent to one**, e.g.,
   $$\frac{2}{3} = \frac{2}{3} \times \left(\frac{3}{3} \right) = \frac{6}{9}$$

We know fractions can be changed, so **how do we change a fraction to a percentage**?

We need to change the denominator to 100. How? By multiplying in a fraction equivalent to **one**.

For instance, if we want to change $\frac{4}{5}$ to a percentage, i.e., so that the denominator is 100, we need to multiply in $\frac{20}{20}$ (since $5 \times 20 = 100$).

$\frac{4}{5}$ then is equal to $\frac{4 \times 20}{5 \times 20}$

$$= \frac{80}{100}$$

$$= 80\%$$

So $\frac{4}{5}$ **is equivalent to 80%**.

There is a shortcut. Look at this:

$$\frac{4}{5} \times 100 = \frac{4}{5} \times \frac{100}{1}$$

$$= \frac{400}{5}$$

$$= 80\%$$

In other words, **to change a fraction into a percentage, multiply it by one hundred**.

Here are some more examples of **fractions being changed to percentages**.

EXAMPLE 1

Change $\frac{3}{10}$ to a percentage.

$$\frac{3}{10} = \left(\frac{3}{10} \times 100 \right)\%$$

$$= \left(\frac{3}{10} \times \frac{100}{1} \right)\%$$

$$= \left(\frac{3 \times 100}{10 \times 1} \right)\%$$

$$= \frac{300}{10}\%$$

$$= 30\% \quad (300 \div 10 = 30)$$

EXAMPLE 2

What is $\frac{3}{20}$ as a percentage?

$$\frac{3}{20} = \left(\frac{3}{20} \times 100\right)\%$$

$$= \left(\frac{3}{20} \times \frac{100}{1}\right)\%$$

$$= \left(\frac{3 \times 100}{20 \times 1}\right)\%$$

$$= \left(\frac{300}{20}\right)\%$$

$$= \left(\frac{30 \times 10}{2 \times 10}\right)\%$$

$$= \left(\frac{30}{2}\right)\% \qquad \text{since } \frac{10}{10} = 1$$

$$= 15\% \quad (30 \div 2 = 15)$$

You may already know that $\frac{1}{4} = 25\%$, that $\frac{1}{2} = 50\%$ and that $\frac{3}{4} = 75\%$.

Here's a table of common fractions and their equivalent in percentages which it is worthwhile for you to **learn**.

Fraction	Percentage
$\frac{1}{10}$	10%
$\frac{1}{5}$	20%
$\frac{1}{4}$	25%
$\frac{1}{2}$	50%
$\frac{3}{4}$	75%
$\frac{4}{5}$	80%

PERCENTAGES TO FRACTIONS

Changing **percentages back to fractions** is **easy**. It's **cancellation** again.

EXAMPLE 3

Change 22% to a fraction.

$$22\% = \frac{22}{100}$$

$$= \frac{2 \times 11}{2 \times 50}$$

$$= \left(\frac{2}{2}\right) \times \left(\frac{11}{50}\right)$$

$$= 1 \times \frac{11}{50}$$

$$= \frac{11}{50}$$

PERCENTAGES TO DESCRIBE SITUATIONS

Percentages are useful in **describing situations**.

EXAMPLE 4

If 6 pupils out of a class of 30 are off sick, what percentage of the class is absent?

First, we make a **fraction** with the number we are interested in *(the number of pupils absent)* as the **numerator** and the total *(number of pupils in the class)* as the **denominator**.

$$\frac{6}{30}$$

To convert this to a percentage, we multiply by 100 as before:

$$\text{Percentage absent} = \left(\frac{6}{30} \times 100 \right) \%$$

$$= \left(\frac{6}{30} \times \frac{100}{1} \right) \%$$

$$= \left(\frac{600}{30} \right) \%$$

$$= 20\%$$

PERCENTAGES FOR MAKING COMPARISONS

Percentages are also a convenient way of making **comparisons**.

EXAMPLE 4

David scored 48 out of 60 in chemistry and 36 out of 40 in maths. What was the better mark?

(*Remember:* we compare the size of two fractions **only when they have a common denominator**. Here the common denominator will effectively be 100.)

Change both to percentages:

Chemistry $= \left(\dfrac{48}{60} \times 100 \right)\%$

$ = \left(\dfrac{48}{60} \times \dfrac{100}{1} \right)\%$

$ = \left(\dfrac{4800}{60} \right)\%$

$ = 80\%$

Maths $= \left(\dfrac{36}{40} \times 100 \right)\%$

$ = \left(\dfrac{36}{40} \times \dfrac{100}{1} \right)\%$

$ = \left(\dfrac{3600}{40} \right)\%$

$ = 90\%$

Mathematics was the better mark.

Exercise 2.3   *(Answers are given on page 53.)*

1. Write these test scores as percentages:

(a) 68 out of 100   *(b)* 40 out of 50   *(c)* 24 / 25   *(d)* 18 / 24

2. Nicola earns £125 a week, of which she saves £25. What percentage of her earnings does she save?

3. 240 plates were delivered to a restaurant but 48 were broken. What percentage of the plates were damaged?

SUMMARY

♦   A percentage is a fraction with 100 as the denominator.

♦   Any fraction can be changed to a percentage by multiplying it by 100.

♦   Any percentage can be changed back into a fraction by cancelling.

♦   Percentages are useful for describing situations and making comparisons.

ANSWERS

Exercise 2.1

(a) 9%   *(b)* 6%   *(c)* 8%   *(d)* 60%   *(e)* 70%   *(f)* 20%

Exercise 2.2

(a) $\dfrac{7}{50}$ *(b)* $\dfrac{6}{25}$ *(c)* $\dfrac{22}{25}$

Exercise 2.3

1.   *(a)* 68%   *(b)* 80%   *(c)* 96%   *(d)* 75%

2.   20%

3.   20%

FINDING A PERCENTAGE OF A NUMBER

We are often asked to find **a percentage of a certain number**.

Buying a car, for instance, might require a 20% deposit or the booking fee for a training course might be 10% of the total bill.

Again, this involves **multiplying fractions**.

Please Note: There are **other** ways of dealing with percentages and these are looked at in the **Decimal Chapter**.

EXAMPLE 1

Find 30% of £210.

$$30\% \text{ of } £210 = £\left(\frac{30}{100} \times \frac{210}{1}\right) \text{ Remember: 'of' means 'multiply'}$$

$$= £\left(\frac{6300}{100}\right)$$

$$= £\left(\frac{63 \times 100}{1 \times 100}\right)$$

$$= £63$$

EXAMPLE 2

Find 8% of 6000 people.

$$8\% \text{ of } 6000 \text{ people} = \left(\frac{8}{100} \times \frac{6000}{1}\right) \text{ people}$$

$$= \left(\frac{48\,000}{100}\right) \text{ people}$$

$$= 480 \text{ people}$$

EXAMPLE 3

What is 7% of 35 kg?

$$7\% \text{ of } 35 \text{ kg} = \left(\frac{7}{100} \times \frac{35}{1}\right) \text{ kg}$$

$$= \left(\frac{245}{100}\right) \text{ kg}$$

$$= 2 \cdot 45 \text{ kg}$$ (Dividing by 100 — shift the decimal point **two places to the left**. Again, see the Decimal section.)

Your turn.

Exercise 2.4   *(Answers are given on page 60.)*

What is:

(a)   40% of £200;   (b)   20% of 1500 people;   (c)   95% of 600;

(d)   1% of £550;   (e)   15% of 500;   (f)   3% of £40 000?

MIXED NUMBER AND FRACTIONAL PERCENTAGES

Consider these statements:

$$\text{Value Added Tax is } 17\frac{1}{2}\%.$$

$$\text{Interest rates look set to rise by } \frac{1}{4}\%.$$

$$\text{Calcium makes up } 3\frac{1}{2}\% \text{ of the Earth's crust.}$$

So far we've only looked at whole number percentages but fractional and mixed number percentages are common.

How do we deal with them?

Let's look at $2\frac{1}{2}\%$ and see what it really **means**.

$$2\frac{1}{2}\% = \frac{2\frac{1}{2}}{100} \qquad \text{(The fraction line means 'divides'.)}$$

$$= 2\frac{1}{2} \div 100$$

$$= \frac{5}{2} \div 100 \qquad \text{(Mixed number to fraction.)}$$

$$= \frac{5}{2} \div \frac{100}{1}$$

$$= \frac{5}{2} \times \frac{1}{100} \qquad \text{(Rule for dividing fractions.)}$$

$$= \frac{5}{200}$$

$$= \frac{1}{40}$$

Here's another way of doing the same thing:

$$2\frac{1}{2}\% = \frac{2\frac{1}{2}}{100}$$

$$2\frac{1}{2}\% = \frac{2\frac{1}{2}}{100} \times \left(\frac{2}{2}\right)$$

$$= \frac{5}{200}$$

$$= \frac{1}{40}$$

Whichever way you choose to approach it, we can now deal with these types of percentages.

EXAMPLE 4

Find $2\frac{1}{2}$ % of £1600.

$$2\frac{1}{2} \text{ % of £1600} = £\left(\frac{5}{200} \times \frac{1600}{1}\right)$$

$$= £\left(\frac{8000}{200}\right)$$

$$= £\left(\frac{80}{2}\right)$$

$$= £40$$

So, to find $3\frac{1}{2}$ % of something, we multiply it by $\left(\frac{7}{2} \times \frac{1}{100}\right) = \frac{7}{200}$.

Similarly, to find $2\frac{1}{2}$ %, multiply by $\left(\frac{5}{2} \times \frac{1}{100}\right) = \frac{5}{200}$;

$17\frac{1}{2}$ % . . . multiply by $\frac{35}{200}$ and so on.

EXAMPLE 5

What is the VAT $\left(\text{at } 17\frac{1}{2} \text{ %}\right)$ on a computer selling in the shop for £1100 plus VAT?

$$\text{VAT} = 17\frac{1}{2} \text{ % of £1100}$$

$$= £\left(\frac{35}{200} \times \frac{1100}{1}\right)$$

$$= £ \frac{35 \times 11 \times 100}{2 \times 1 \times 100}$$

$$= £ \frac{35 \times 11}{2}$$

$$= £ \frac{385}{2}$$

$$= £192.50$$

In exactly the same way,

$$\text{to find } \tfrac{1}{2}\%, \text{ multiply by } \left(\tfrac{1}{2} \times \tfrac{1}{100}\right) = \tfrac{1}{200}$$

$$\text{to find } \tfrac{1}{4}\%, \text{ multiply by } \left(\tfrac{1}{4} \times \tfrac{1}{100}\right) = \tfrac{1}{400}$$

$$\text{to find } \tfrac{3}{4}\%, \text{ multiply by } \left(\tfrac{3}{4} \times \tfrac{1}{100}\right) = \tfrac{3}{400}$$

and so on.

EXAMPLE 6

Find $\tfrac{1}{4}\%$ of 16 800.

$$
\begin{aligned}
\tfrac{1}{4}\% \text{ of } 16\,800 &= \left(\tfrac{1}{4} \times \tfrac{1}{100}\right) \times 16\,800 \\
&= \frac{16\,800}{4 \times 100} \\
&= \frac{168}{4} \\
&= 42
\end{aligned}
$$

Here's some for you to try.

Exercise 2.5 *(Answers are given on page 60.)*

What is:

(a) $1\tfrac{1}{2}\%$ of 4000;

(b) $\tfrac{3}{4}\%$ of 100 000;

(c) $2\tfrac{1}{2}\%$ of 800;

(d) $2\tfrac{3}{4}\%$ of 8800;

(e) $8\tfrac{1}{2}\%$ of 1200;

(f) $17\tfrac{1}{2}\%$ of £40 000?

SUMMARY

♦ To find a percentage of a given number, we multiply the percentage (written as a fraction) by that number. Since every number can be written as **itself over one**, this is the same as multiplying two fractions together.

♦ Mixed number and fractional percentages are first divided by 100 to produce a new fraction and then the same process of multiplication is used.

ANSWERS

Exercise 2.4

(a) £80   *(b)* 300 people   *(c)* 570   *(d)* £5.50   *(e)* 75   *(f)* £1200

Exercise 2.5

(a) 60   *(b)* 750   *(c)* 20   *(d)* 242   *(e)* 102   *(f)* £7000

PERCENTAGES THAT DESCRIBE CHANGE

Percentages are often used to describe a **change**, either an **increase** or a **decrease**, on a previous position.

EXAMPLE 1

Chloe earns £180 a week but has just been told her pay will increase by 20%.

(a) How much extra money will she earn?

(b) What will be her new wage?

(a) The extra amount will be 20% of £180.

$$20\% \text{ of } £180 = £\left(\frac{20}{100} \times \frac{180}{1}\right)$$

$$= £\left(\frac{20 \times 180}{100 \times 1}\right)$$

$$= £\left(\frac{20 \times 180}{20 \times 5}\right)$$

$$= £\left(\frac{180}{5}\right)$$

$$= £36 \qquad (180 \div 5 = 36)$$

(b) Her new wage will be her old wage + her increase $= £180 + £36$

$$= £216$$

EXAMPLE 2

A company director whose firm is in crisis accepts a cut in salary. He was being paid £110 000 a year but agreed to take 15% less.

(a) By how much is his salary reduced?

(b) What is his new salary?

(a) The reduction is 15% of £110 000.

$$15\% \text{ of } £110\,000 = £\left(\frac{15}{100} \times \frac{110\,000}{1}\right)$$

$$= £\left(\frac{15 \times 1100 \times 100}{100 \times 1}\right)$$

$$= £(15 \times 1100)$$

$$= £16\,500$$

(b) The new salary is the old salary – the reduction $= £110\,000 - £16\,500$

$$= £93\,500$$

Now here's some for you to try.

Exercise 2.6   *(Answers are given on page 65.)*

1.   What is:

(a)   £50 increased by 20%;

(b)   180 litres decreased by 15%?

2.   Calum earns £4.00 per hour cleaning windows. He is so good at it that six months later his rate of pay has increased by 75%. What is his new hourly rate?

3.   A local radio station has been giving away coupons to listeners offering 5% discount in certain stores. How much can a lucky listener **expect to pay** for:

(a)   a pair of designer label jeans normally selling for £80;

(b)   a washing machine usually priced at £180?

4.   The government recently announced a 6% increase in the salary of new teachers.

If they used to get £16 000 a year, what is their new salary?

Of course the fractional and mixed number percentages we looked at in the last section are also commonly used to describe an increase or decrease.

EXAMPLE 2

Property prices in a part of Edinburgh rose by $1\frac{1}{4}$ % in the year 2000. If a typical two-bedroom flat was priced at £40 000 at the end of 1999, what price would you expect it to fetch in 2001?

$$\text{Price rise} \;=\; 1\frac{1}{4}\% \text{ of £40 000}$$

$$= £\left(\frac{5}{400} \times \frac{40\,000}{1}\right)$$

$$= £\left(\frac{5 \times 400 \times 100}{400 \times 1}\right)$$

$$= £(5 \times 100)$$

$$= £500$$

$$\text{Price expected in 2001} \;=\; \text{1999 price + price rise}$$

$$= £40\,000 + £500$$

$$= £40\,500$$

Exercise 2.7   *(Answers are given on page 65.)*

1. A small craft shop saw an increase in profits of $2\frac{1}{4}$ % last year. Profits had been steady at £8000 for several years.

    How much **extra** profit is that?

2. A popular Scottish tourist attraction had a $\frac{1}{2}$ % drop in visitor numbers in 2001 compared to the previous year.

    If 120 000 people visited the attraction in 2000, how many came in 2001?

SUMMARY

♦ Percentages are often used to indicate a **change**, either an **increase** or a **decrease** on a previous position.

♦ To find out how much has changed, we multiply the percentage (written as a fraction) by the old figure.

♦ To find out the new figure, we add the change to the old figure if it is an increase or subtract it if it is a decrease.

♦ Fractional and mixed number percentages can be treated in the same way as whole number percentages.

ANSWERS

Exercise 2.6

1.	*(a)*	£60	*(b)*	153 litres
2.	£7.00			
3.	*(a)*	£76	*(b)*	£171
4.	£16 960			

Exercise 2.7

1. £180
2. 119 400 people

CHANGE DESCRIBED BY A PERCENTAGE

We have seen how percentages are used to describe change, so obviously, any **change** can be described by a **percentage**.

How do we do that?

By making a fraction with the **change as the numerator and the old situation as the denominator**. The fraction becomes a percentage when multiplied by 100.

Here are some examples.

EXAMPLE 1

A factory worker earning £200 a week gets a promotion and a pay rise of £40 a week.

What percentage rise is that?

$$\text{Percentage rise} = (\text{change} \div \text{old} \times 100)\%$$

$$= \left(\frac{40}{200} \times \frac{100}{1} \right)\%$$

$$= \left(\frac{40 \times 100}{2 \times 100} \right)\%$$

$$= \left(\frac{40}{2} \right)\%$$

$$= 20\%$$

EXAMPLE 2

Jonathon paid £80 for a pair of trainers normally priced at £200.

What percentage discount did he get?

Here, the change is the difference in price. £200 − £80 = £120 which is the amount the trainers have been discounted.

Percentage discount = (change ÷ old × 100)%

$$= \left(\frac{120}{200} \times \frac{100}{1} \right)\%$$

$$= \left(\frac{120 \times 100}{2 \times 100} \right)\%$$

$$= \left(\frac{120}{2} \right)\%$$

$$= 60\%$$

EXAMPLE 3

Grant paid £75 for a CD player but sold it in a car boot sale six months later for £45.

As a percentage, how much money did he lose?

In this example the change is the amount of money Grant lost, i.e., £75 − £45 = £30.

Percentage loss = (change ÷ old × 100)%

$$= \left(\frac{30}{75} \times \frac{100}{1} \right)\%$$

$$= \left(\frac{3 \times 10 \times 25 \times 4}{3 \times 25} \right)\%$$

$$= (10 \times 4)\%$$

$$= 40\%$$

Over to you.

Exercise 2.8 *(Answers are given on page 73.)*

1. David had a salary rise of £400. If his salary had been £16 000, what percentage rise is this?

2. A special offer on a set of wrenches from a DIY store is £1 off the normal price of £8.00. What percentage discount is this?

3. Rory is eleven months old and in the last six months his height has increased from 75 cm to 105 cm. What percentage increase is this?

PERCENTAGES GREATER THAN ONE HUNDRED

The coach tells the team he wants 101% effort, thinking that he is expecting more than is humanly possible as percentages only go up to 100.

Not so. It can make sense to have percentages more than 100. An increase of 150% just means the same amount again (100%) + 50% (half as much).

And, just like other percentages, 150% can be written as a fraction: $\frac{150}{100}$.

EXAMPLE 4

In its first year, a company had profits of £80 000. In the following year, profits rose by 150%. What were the profits in the second year?

$$\text{Profits in second year } = £\left(\frac{80\,000}{1} \times \frac{150}{100}\right)$$
$$= £(800 \times 150)$$
$$= £120\,000$$

Note: £120 000 = £80 000 + £40 000
$$= \quad 100\% \quad + \quad 50\%$$

Of course a company can have a similar **decrease** in profits, but **they can no longer be called profits!**

EXAMPLE 5

A company sees profits fall by 120% in the last twelve months. If the profits had previously been £100 000, what is the current situation?

Profits last year $= \pounds 100\ 000$

$$= \pounds\left(\frac{120}{100} \times \frac{100\ 000}{1}\right)$$

$$= \pounds 120\ 000$$

Current profits $=$ old $-$ new

$$= \pounds 100\ 000 - \pounds 120\ 000$$

$$= -\pounds 20\ 000 \ldots \textbf{Oh dear!}$$

Exercise 2.9 *(Answers are given on page 73.)*

A winery increases its production from 20 000 bottles by 115% in two years.

(a)   What is the increase in the number of bottles produced?

(b)   What is the production level after the two year period?

INVERSE PERCENTAGE CALCULATIONS

So far we have seen the results of quantities being increased or decreased by a percentage. What if we are given an amount having been told that it has been increased or decreased by a certain percentage and are then asked to find the **original** amount? This is called an inverse percentage calculation.

To understand this sort of calculation, there are two things to bear in mind.

First, the original amount is always defined as 100%.

For example if an airline ticked is reduced by 25% from £800 to £600, £800 represents 100%.

Second, there is another way of looking at percentage change. The previous example is used to explain:

$$\begin{aligned}
\text{new price} &= 100\% \text{ of £800} - 25\% \text{ of £800} \\
&= (100\% - 25\%) \text{ of £800} \\
&= 75\% \text{ of £800} \\
&= £\left(\frac{75}{100} \times 800 \right) \\
&= £600
\end{aligned}$$

In other words, new price $= \frac{75}{100} \times$ old price.

This idea of the new amount being some fraction $\left(\text{in this case } \frac{75}{100} \right)$ of the old amount is useful in inverse percentage calculations, but a little algebra is also called for. Study the following example carefully.

EXAMPLE 6

In the last two years, the price of a house in Scotland has increased by 32% and is now worth £264 000. What was it worth two years ago?

Note: The easiest mistake in the world to make is to find 32% of £264 000 but the increase of 32% is based on the *original* price (as yet unknown).

Here's the algebra:

Call the original price **x**.

$$\begin{aligned}
\text{New price} &= 100\% \text{ of } \boldsymbol{x} + 32\% \text{ of } \boldsymbol{x} \\
264\,000 &= 132\% \text{ of } \boldsymbol{x} \\
&= \frac{132}{100} \times \boldsymbol{x}
\end{aligned}$$

Now we need to get x on its own, i.e., we need to *divide* both sides of this equation by $\frac{132}{100}$, which as we have seen means *multiplying* both sides by $\frac{100}{132}$:

$$264\,000 \times \frac{100}{132} = \frac{132}{100} \times x \times \frac{100}{132}$$

i.e., $\qquad \frac{264\,000 \times 100}{132} = x$

i.e., $\qquad\qquad\quad x = 2000 \times 100$

$$= 200\,000$$

Two years ago the house was worth £200 000.

EXAMPLE 7

In a sale where everything is marked down by 20%, a CD sells for £10. What was its usual price?

Let x be the usual (old) price.

$$\text{New price} = 100\% \text{ of old price} - 20\% \text{ of old price}$$

$$10 = 100\% \text{ of } x - 20\% \text{ of } x$$

$$10 = 80\% \text{ of } x$$

$$10 = \frac{80}{100} \times x$$

$$10 \times \frac{100}{80} = \frac{80}{100} \times x \times \frac{100}{80}$$

$$\frac{10 \times 100}{80} = x$$

$$x = \frac{100}{8}$$

$$= 12\tfrac{1}{2}$$

The usual price for the CD is £12.50.

Exercise 2.10   *(Answers are given on page 73.)*

1.   Hannah had a wage rise of 10% which gave her a salary of £220 per week. What was her old wage?

2.   After a 15% reduction, Nina's bike cost £425. What was its usual price?

3.   The mark-up on wine in a restaurant is 50% of the usual retail price. If a bottle of Cabernet Sauvignon costs £45 on the wine list, what can Christopher expect to pay for it in the shops?

4.   Clay loses 12% of its weight when it is fired in a kiln. If a statue weighs 264 g after firing, what was its original weight?

5.   In Scotland, whisky must be aged ten years in which time 6% of the spirit is lost through evaporation. If 188 litres of whisky remain in a ten year old cask, how much spirit has been lost?

SUMMARY

♦   Change can be described as a percentage by making a fraction with the new amount as the numerator, the old amount as the denominator and then multiplying by one hundred.

♦   Percentages can be more than one hundred.

♦   Percentage change can also be expressed as a fraction of the original amount and an inverse percentage calculation uses division of this fraction.

ANSWERS

Exercise 2.8

1. $2\frac{1}{2}\%$

2. $12\frac{1}{2}\%$

3.   40% increase

Exercise 2.9

(a)   23 000 bottles   *(b)*   43 000 bottles

Exercise 2.10

1.   £200
2.   £500
3.   £30
4.   300 g
5.   12 litres

TEST ON PERCENTAGES

The only way to be sure that you have mastered percentages is to test yourself.

So here are thirteen questions worth a total of 33 marks. When you've finished, you can check how well you've done because the answers are on the following page.

Marks

1. Write as a percentage:

    (a) $\frac{2}{5}$; (b) $\frac{18}{20}$. **2**

2. Write as a fraction:

    (a) 15% (b) 16% **2**

3. Write these two test results as percentages and decide which was the better mark.

    French: 11 out of 25 English: 9 out of 20 **2**

4. There are 600 pupils attending a primary school. Thirty contract meningitis. What percentage of the school's population is affected? **2**

5. What is

    (a) 60% of 700? (b) 12% of 3000? **2**

6. What is

    (a) $1\frac{1}{2}$ % of 200? (b) $\frac{1}{4}$ % of 2000? **2**

7. Jamie's wage has risen by 24% in twelve months. If he had been earning £5 an hour, what is his new hourly rate of pay? **3**

8. Powerplant, an electricity generator, intends to reduce its workforce by 12%. If there are currently 3000 people employed at the plant, how many will be working there after the plan has been implemented? **3**

9. The average temperature for June in Britain is expected to increase by $1\frac{1}{2}$ % over the next one hundred years. If the average June temperature for 2000 was 20 °C, what is the average temperature expected for June in the year 2100? **3**

10. A call centre currently employs 2400 people but intends to expand that to 2460. What percentage increase to the workforce is this?　　**3**

11. Over twelve months, a fisherman notes that his haul of haddock has dropped from 40 boxes to 33 boxes. What percentage decrease is this?　　**3**

12. Lyndsey's salary has increased by 9% to £17 440. What was her salary before the increase?　　**3**

13. A sports store has a closing down sale advertising 30% off everything. Caroline buys a set of golf clubs for £119. What would the set have cost her normally?　　**3**

Total marks (33)

ANSWERS

1. *(a)* 40%   *(b)* 90%   **2** (1 mark each)

2. *(a)* $\frac{15}{100} = \frac{3}{20}$ *(b)* $\frac{16}{100} = \frac{4}{25}$ **2**

3. $\frac{11}{25} = 44\%$, $\frac{9}{20} = 45\%$. English is the better mark.   **2**

4. 5%   **2**

5. *(a)* 420   *(b)* 360   **2**

6. *(a)* 3   *(b)* 5   **2**

7. £6.20   **3**

8. 2640   **3**

9. 20·3 °C   **3**

10. $2\frac{1}{2}\%$ **3**

11. $17\frac{1}{2}\%$ **3**

12. £16 000   **3**

13. £170   **3**

Total marks (33)

INTERPRETING YOUR TEST SCORE

Less than 16   You still have not understood the fundamentals of percentages and you need more help.

16 to 23   The basics are there but more practice is needed on the weak areas.

24 to 29   A good understanding of the subject which should see you through.

30+   Congratulations! You have mastered percentages!

CHAPTER 3

DECIMALS

PLACE VALUE

The word 'decimal' comes from the Latin *decem* meaning 'ten'. Our number system is based on ten. All numbers less than ten (sometimes called **units**) have their own symbol:

> 0, 1, 2, 3, 4, 5, 6, 7, 8 and 9 but ten is written '10' meaning 'one (ten) (plus) zero (units)'.

> Two hundred and fifteen is written as 215 meaning 'two (hundreds) (plus) one (ten) (plus) five (units)'.

All numbers are written in this way so that each individual number (digit) in any written number has a **place value based on ten**.

A **decimal point** is a dot placed in a number to separate the digits into place values **greater than one** (to the **left** of the decimal point) and those **less than one** (to the **right** of the decimal point).

The digits with place value less than one are sometimes called **decimal places**.

To the **left** of the decimal point each place value is **ten times greater than the one before it**. To the **right** of the decimal point, (decimal places), each place value is **a tenth of the value of the place before it**.

The order is hundreds of thousands, tens of thousands, thousands, hundreds, tens, units (DP) tenths, hundredths, thousandths . . .

For example, in the number one hundred and thirty-two thousand, five hundred and forty six, 132 546, there are no digits of place value less than one.

The place value of the other digits are:

Digit	Place Value
6	Ones (Units)
4	Tens
5	Hundreds
2	Thousands
3	Tens of Thousands
1	Hundreds of Thousands

Look at the number 32·546. It has three decimal places (place values less than one . . . 5, 4 and 6) and the digits have the following place values:

Digit	Place Value
3	Tens
2	Ones (Units)
5	Tenths
4	Hundredths
6	Thousandths

When a number is written **without a decimal point**, we assume that it is at the **right hand end** of the number:

210 = 210·0 (we add in a zero rather than write 210·), not 2·10 or 0·210.

Exercise 3.1   *(Answers are given on page 83.)*

1.   What is the place value of 6 in:

   (a)   622·2   *(b)*   0·06   *(c)*   0·624

   (d)   65·3   *(e)*   6·219   *(f)*   0·006

2.   How many decimal places are there in each of the numbers in 1 *(a)* to *(f)*?

MULTIPLYING AND DIVIDING BY 10, 100 AND 1000

Because our number system is based on ten, multiplying and dividing by ten (and one hundred, one thousand, etc.) is **easy**!

To multiply by ten, shift the decimal point one place to the right.

EXAMPLE 1

Multiply 39·27 by ten.

$$39·27 \times 10 = 3\,9·2\,7 = 392·7$$

EXAMPLE 2

Multiply 0·003927 by ten.

$$0·003927 \times 10 = 0·0\,0\,3\,9\,2\,7 = 0·03927$$

To divide by ten, shift the decimal point one place to the left.

EXAMPLE 3

Divide 541·9 by ten.

$$541·9 \div 10 = 5\,4\,1·9 = 54·19$$

EXAMPLE 4

Divide 0·5419 by ten.

$$0·5419 \div 10 = 0·5419 = 0·05419$$

Multiplication and division by one hundred or one thousand is just as easy.

To **multiply by one hundred**, shift the decimal point **two places** to the **right**.

To **divide by one hundred**, shift the decimal point **two places** to the **left**.

To **multiply by one thousand**, shift the decimal point **three places** to the **right**.

To **divide by one thousand**, shift the decimal point **three places** to the **left**.

EXAMPLE 5

Multiply 49·05 by 100.

$$49·05 \times 100 = 49·05 = 4905$$

EXAMPLE 6

Divide 4905 by 1000.

$$4905 \div 1000 = 4905 = 4·905$$

(**Note** that no decimal point is indicated in the number 4905, so we assume it is on the right, 4905·0.)

Sometimes we 'run out of numbers' when shifting the decimal point. Zeros are inserted as 'place holders'.

EXAMPLE 7

Multiply 4·7 by 100.

$$4·7 \times 100 = 4·70 = 470$$

(**Note** that since the decimal point is now at the end of the number, it need not be written down.)

EXAMPLE 8

Divide 4·72 by 1000.

$$4·72 \div 1000 = 004·72 = 0·00472$$

Exercise 3.2   *(Answers are given on page 83.)*

Simplify:

1	*(a)*	30·2 × 10	*(b)*	0·02 × 100	*(c)*	0·309 × 1000
2.	*(a)*	54·4 ÷ 10	*(b)*	569 ÷ 1000	*(c)*	0·19 ÷ 100

SUMMARY

♦ Every **digit** in a number has a **place value**.

♦ To the **left** of the decimal point:
    units, tens, hundreds, thousands, tens of thousands.

♦ To the **right** of the decimal point:
    tenths, hundredths, thousandths.

♦ **Digits to the right** of the decimal point are also called **decimal places**.

♦ **Multiplying** by ten, one hundred or one thousand involves shifting the decimal point to the **right**.

♦ **Dividing** by ten, one hundred or one thousand involves shifting the decimal point to the **left**.

♦ For **ten**, move the decimal point **one** place.

♦ For **one hundred**, move the decimal point **two** places.

♦ For **one thousand**, move the decimal point **three** places.

ANSWERS

Exercise 3.1

1. *(a)* one hundred   *(b)* one hundredth   *(c)* one tenth
   (d) ten   *(e)* one (unit)   *(f)* one thousandth

2. *(a)* 1   *(b)* 2   *(c)* 3   *(d)* 1   *(e)* 3   *(f)* 3

Exercise 3.2

1. *(a)* 302   *(b)* 2   *(c)* 309

2. *(a)* 5·44   *(b)* 0·569   *(c)* 0·0019

ADDING AND SUBTRACTING DECIMALS

When **adding** or **subtracting** decimals, it is essential to **keep the decimal place and all digits of equal place value directly underneath one another**.

It's done like this.

EXAMPLE 1

Add: $212 \cdot 2 + 0 \cdot 03 + 2 \cdot 15 + 0 \cdot 6 + 12$

$$
\begin{array}{r}
212 \cdot 20 \\
0 \cdot 03 \\
2 \cdot 15 \\
0 \cdot 60 \\
+12 \cdot 00 \\
\hline
226 \cdot 98 \\
\hline
\end{array}
$$

Notice that extra zeros were put in on some numbers to avoid confusion about the correct place values of the digits but the most important point to note is that **all digits of the same value lie directly beneath each other**.

EXAMPLE 2

Add: $49 + 5 \cdot 92 + 10 \cdot 1 + 0 \cdot 09 + 101 \cdot 01$

$$
\begin{array}{r}
49 \cdot 00 \\
5 \cdot 92 \\
10 \cdot 10 \\
0 \cdot 09 \\
+101 \cdot 01 \\
\hline
166 \cdot 12 \\
\hline
\end{array}
$$

Your turn.

Exercise 3.3 *(Answers are given on page 90.)*

(a)   Add: $1·08 + 1·2 + 0·3 + 56·2$

(b)   Add: $102·07 + 0·08 + 11·2 + 47·6$

Exactly the same idea is used with **subtraction**.

EXAMPLE 3

Subtract 0·521 from 11·09

$$
\begin{array}{r}
11·090 \\
-0·521 \\
\hline
10·569
\end{array}
$$

And now over to you again.

Exercise 3.4 *(Answers are given on page 90.)*

(a)   Subtract 0·075 from 1·209

(b)   Subtract 1·13 from 22·5

MULTIPLYING AND DIVIDING DECIMALS

Multiplication of decimals works in a different way. **The number of decimal places in the numbers being multiplied decides how many decimal places there will be in the final answer**.

Here's how it works:

EXAMPLE 4

Multiply 3·05 by 0·2.

> First we decide how many decimal places are involved in the two numbers being multiplied
>
> $$3·05 \quad \text{TWO} \quad (0, 5)$$
> $$0·2 \quad \text{ONE} \quad (2).$$
>
> Total = **THREE decimal places**.
>
> Having done that, we go ahead with multiplying the numbers in the usual way, ignoring the decimal points completely until the end.

$$
\begin{array}{r}
3 \cdot 0\,5 \\
\times \quad 0 \cdot 2 \\
\hline
6\,1\,0 \\
0\,0\,0\,0 \\
\hline
0\,6\,1\,0 \\
\end{array}
$$

Where to put the decimal point?

There are THREE decimal places in the question, so there will be THREE decimal places in the answer. We start from the right hand side and count three places to the left:

0 6 1 0

The answer is 0·610.

EXAMPLE 5

Multiply 61·35 by 1·01.

```
      6 1 · 3 5      Two decimal places
  ×     1 · 0 1      Two decimal places.
  _____             Total = four decimal places.
      6 1 3 5
    0 0 0 0 0
  6 1 3 5 0 0
  _____
  6 1 9 6 3 5
  _____
```

6 1 9 6 3 5

The answer is 61·9635.

Here's some for you to try:

Exercise 3.5 *(Answers are given on page 90.)*

Multiply:

(a) 0·82 by 0·005

(b) 7·04 by 2·1

Division by decimals needs a different strategy. The rule is that **division is only possible with a whole number**, i.e., no decimal places. We need to change the dividing number **and** the number which is being divided by the **same amount** (so that the final answer is unaffected).

We have already seen the decimal point moving when a number is multiplied by ten, one hundred or one thousand. Here it is used to turn a decimal number into a whole number.

Watch it being done.

EXAMPLE 6

What is 906·3 ÷ 0·3?

$$0.3 \overline{)906.3}$$

As it stands at the moment, it is not possible to proceed. 0·3 needs to become 3, i.e., it needs to be multiplied by **ten**. That being the case, 906·3 **also** needs to be multiplied by ten.

$$0 \cdot 3^{\curvearrowright} \qquad 9\,0\,6 \cdot 3^{\curvearrowright}$$

The net result:

$$3 \overline{)9063}$$

Now we can go ahead in the usual way:

$$\begin{array}{r} 3021 \\ 3 \overline{)9063} \end{array}$$

So, 906·3 ÷ 0·3 = 3021

We have seen something like this already in **Fractions**. Here's why it works.

$$906·3 \div 0·3 = \frac{906·3}{0·3}$$

$$= \frac{906·3}{0·3} \times \left(\frac{10}{10}\right)$$

$$= \frac{9063}{3}$$

$$= 9063 \div 3$$

EXAMPLE 7

What is 7·47 ÷ 0·03?

Here, 0·03 needs to be multiplied by 100 so that the decimal place shifts two places to the right. Similarly, 7·47 must be multiplied by 100. If we go ahead and do that we have:

$$747 \div 3$$

which we then solve:

$$\begin{array}{r} 249 \\ 3\overline{)747} \end{array}$$

So, 7·47 ÷ 0·03 = 249

Exercise 3.6   *(Answers are given on page 90.)*

What is:

(a)   8·8 ÷ 0·4?   *(b)*   28·75 ÷ 0·05?

SUMMARY

♦   When **adding** or **subtracting** decimal numbers, the **decimal points of each number must be directly underneath one another** so that all digits of equal place value are also underneath each other.

♦   When **multiplying** decimal numbers, the **total number of decimal places involved** needs to be found. In the final answer, this number decides the correct position of the decimal place, counting from the right.

♦   When **division** by a decimal is required, **both** numbers need to be changed so that the **divisor becomes a whole number**.

ANSWERS

Exercise 3.3

(a)   58·78   *(b)*   160·95

Exercise 3.4

(a)   1·134   *(b)*   21·37

Exercise 3.5

(a)   0·0041   *(b)*   14·784

Exercise 3.6

(a)   22   *(b)*   575

DECIMALS TO FRACTIONS

Fractions and decimals are different ways of representing the same number.

Any decimal can be written as a fraction.

Take 0·3 for instance.

We can see that this is the result of the number three being divided by ten because the decimal point has shifted one place to the left. So,

$$0·3 = \frac{3}{10}$$ Remember the fraction line means 'divide'.

In the same way, 0·31 is 31 ÷ 100

$$0·31 = \frac{31}{100}$$

and similarly

$$0·312 = \frac{312}{1000}$$

If a fraction can be cancelled down, then it must be done, for instance,

$$0·8 = \frac{8}{10} = \frac{4 \times 2}{5 \times 2} = \frac{4}{5}$$

Decimal numbers greater than one can be written as mixed numbers. Here are some examples.

$$1·5 \quad = 1\frac{5}{10} = 1\frac{1}{2}$$

$$2·7 \quad = 2\frac{7}{10}$$

$$27·13 = 27\frac{13}{100}$$

Exercise 3.7   *(Answers are given on page 96.)*

Express as fractions (cancel down if necessary).

(a) 0·9   *(b)* 0·009   *(c)* 1·75   *(d)* 31·2

FRACTIONS TO DECIMALS

You may already know that $\frac{1}{2}$ is the same as 0·5, $\frac{1}{4}$ is the same as 0·25 and $\frac{3}{4}$ is equivalent to 0·75. In fact, **any fraction can be turned into a decimal by dividing the numerator by the denominator**, i.e., 'the bottom number divides into the top number'.

Remember: The fraction line means 'divides'.

EXAMPLE 1

Write $\frac{7}{8}$ as a decimal.

$$\begin{array}{r} 0{\cdot}875 \\ 8\overline{)7000} \end{array}$$

Since 8 will not divide into 7, a decimal point is placed above it and the question becomes 'how many times does 8 divide into 70?' Since $8 \times 8 = 64$, the answer is 8, remainder 4. This 4 is carried forward on to the next digit (zero) to become 40. 8 is then divided into 40. It will divide exactly 5 times with no remainder.

This is called 'short' division. You may be more familiar with 'long' division, so here it is done again.

$$\begin{array}{r} 0{\cdot}875 \\ 8\overline{)7000} \\ \underline{64} \\ 60 \\ \underline{56} \\ 40 \\ \underline{40} \\ 0 \end{array}$$

EXAMPLE 2

What is $3\frac{2}{5}$ written as a decimal?

Here, we get the fraction part as a decimal first then add three to the answer.

$$5\overline{)20} \quad \to \quad 0\cdot4$$

So, $3\frac{2}{5}$ = 3·4 as a decimal.

Or we could just as easily do it this way:

$$3\frac{2}{5} = \frac{17}{5}$$

$$= 17 \div 5$$

$$= 3\cdot4$$

Exercise 3.8 *(Answers are given on page 96.)*

Write as decimals.

(a) $\frac{1}{5}$ (b) $\frac{1}{8}$ (c) $2\frac{1}{4}$ (d) $1\frac{3}{5}$

ROUNDING OFF

Very often the division does not give us the neat results we have just seen.

For instance,

$$\frac{1}{3} = 0.33333333333\ldots$$

$$\frac{5}{6} = 0.83333333333\ldots \quad \text{and even worse}$$

$$\frac{6}{7} = 0.857142857142\ldots$$

These are known as repeating decimals and to keep things sensible, we shorten them or **round them off**.

To round off to a particular decimal place we need to look at the next digit to the right.

If that digit is between 0 and 4, we leave the new number just as it is.

If the next digit is between 5 and 9, the last digit of the new number has to go up by one.

These examples show the thinking behind the process of 'rounding off'.

EXAMPLE 3

Round 0.83333 . . . to two decimal places.

0.833333

Round to here. Note the next digit is 3, so the number stays the **same**.

0.83333 . . . to two decimal places is 0.83

EXAMPLE 4

Round 0.8570142 . . . to one decimal place.

0.8570142

Round off to here. The next digit is 5, so we need to round 8 **up by one**.

0.8570142 . . . 0.9 to one decimal place.

EXAMPLE 5

Round 0·857142 to two decimal places.

      0·857142
        ↑

      Round to here. The next digit is 7, so the 5 needs to go up by **one**.

0·857142 = 0·86 to two decimal places.

EXAMPLE 6

Round 0·857142 to three decimal places.

      0·857142
        ↑

      Round to here. The next digit is 1, so the number **stays the same**.

0·857142 = 0·857 to three decimal places.

Exercise 3.9   *(Answers are given on page 96.)*

1.   Round these numbers off to two decimal places:

     (a) 2·241   *(b)* 9·4942   *(c)* 8·829

2.   Round the above numbers to one decimal place.

SUMMARY

♦   When 'rounding off' a decimal, the next digit is important. If it is between 0 and 4, the new number stays the same. If it is between 5 and 9, the last digit of the new number goes up by one.

♦   A fraction can be written as a decimal and a decimal as a fraction.

ANSWERS

Exercise 3.7

(a) $\dfrac{9}{10}$

(b) $\dfrac{9}{1000}$

(c) $1\dfrac{3}{4}$

(d) $31\dfrac{1}{5}$

Exercise 3.8

(a) 0·2

(b) 0·125

(c) 2·25

(d) 1·6

Exercise 3.9

1. (a) 2·24

    (b) 9·49

    (c) 8·83

2. (a) 2·2

    (b) 9·5

    (c) 8·8

DECIMALS TO PERCENTAGES

You will recall that a percentage is a special fraction with one hundred as the denominator.

For instance, $30\% = \dfrac{30}{100}$

Remember too that any fraction can be expressed as a percentage simply by multiplying it by one hundred.

$$
\begin{aligned}
\frac{4}{5} &= \left(\frac{4}{5} \times 100 \right)\% \\
&= \left(\frac{4}{5} \times \frac{100}{1} \right)\% \\
&= \left(\frac{4 \times 100}{5 \times 1} \right)\% \\
&= \left(\frac{400}{5} \right)\% \\
&= 80\% \qquad (400 \div 5 = 80)
\end{aligned}
$$

Because we have already seen that **any decimal** can be written as a **fraction**, and any **fraction** can be written as a **percentage**, it follows that **any decimal can also be written as a percentage**.

As with fractions, **to change a decimal to a percentage, multiply it by one hundred**. (Putting it another way, shift the decimal point two places to the right.)

Here are some examples to show it being done.

EXAMPLE 1

Express 0·3 as a percentage.

$$
\begin{aligned}
0\cdot3 &= (0\cdot3 \times 100)\% \\
&= 30\%
\end{aligned}
$$

EXAMPLE 2

What is 0·425 as a percentage?

$$0.425 = (0.425 \times 100)\%$$
$$= 42.5\%$$

PERCENTAGES TO DECIMALS

Of course it works the other way too. **Any percentage can also be written as a decimal by dividing it by one hundred**.

(In other words, shift the decimal point two places to the left.)

EXAMPLE 3

What is 35% as a decimal?

$$35\% = \frac{35}{100}$$
$$= 35 \div 100$$
$$= 0.35$$

EXAMPLE 4

Express 2% as a decimal.

$$2\% = \frac{2}{100}$$
$$= 2 \div 100$$
$$= 0.02$$

Mixed number percentages can be easily expressed as decimals too.

EXAMPLE 5

What is $1\frac{1}{4}$ % as a decimal?

$$1\frac{1}{4}\% = \frac{1.25}{100} \quad \textbf{or} \quad \frac{5}{4} \times \frac{1}{100} = \frac{5}{400}$$
$$= 0.0125 \qquad\qquad\qquad = 0.0125$$

EXAMPLE 6

Express $17\frac{1}{2}$ % as a decimal.

$$17\frac{1}{2}\% = \frac{17 \cdot 5}{100}$$
$$= 0 \cdot 175$$

Exercise 3.10 *(Answers are given on page 106.)*

1. Express as decimal.

    (a) 28%   *(b)* 40%   *(c)* 4%   *(d)* 97·5%

2. Express as percentage.

    (a) 0·14   *(b)* 0·06   *(c)* 0·03   *(d)* 0·025

Below is a chart showing some frequently used fractions and equivalents as percentages and decimals.

Fraction	Percentage	Decimal
$\frac{1}{10}$	10%	0·10
$\frac{1}{5}$	20%	0·20
$\frac{1}{4}$	25%	0·25
$\frac{1}{2}$	50%	0·50
$\frac{3}{4}$	75%	0·75
$\frac{4}{5}$	80%	0·80

As we have seen, fractions, percentages and decimals are all essentially the same. The diagram below is a summary of the ways in which they are related and how they can be changed from one form to another.

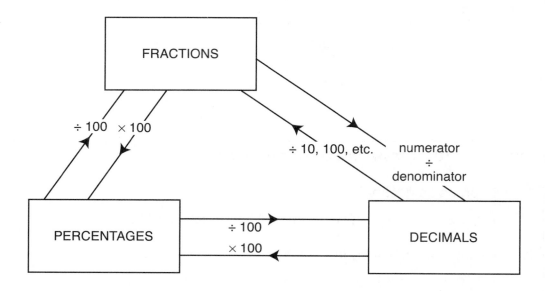

FINDING PERCENTAGES USING 1%

We have seen division by one hundred is an easy operation and it is especially useful in finding percentages.

First, it's important to note that **dividing a number by one hundred is the same as finding one per cent of that number**.

Here are two examples.

EXAMPLE 7

What is 1% of 224?

$$1\% \text{ of } 224 = 224 \div 100$$

$$= 2\,2\,4 \cdot 0$$

$$= 2 \cdot 24$$

EXAMPLE 8

Find 1% of 23.

$$1\% \text{ of } 23 = 23 \div 100$$

$$= {}^{1}23 \cdot 0$$

$$= 0 \cdot 23$$

Having found **one** per cent of a number, it is easy then to find **any other** percentage of that number.

Here are two examples to show how it's done.

EXAMPLE 9

What is 18% of 2456?

$$1\% \text{ of } 2456 = 2456 \div 100$$

$$= 24 \cdot 56$$

$$18\% \text{ of } 2456 = 18 \times 1\% \text{ of } 2456$$

$$= 18 \times 24 \cdot 56$$

$$= 442 \cdot 08$$

$$
\begin{array}{r}
24 \cdot 56 \\
\times \quad 18 \\
\hline
19648 \\
24560 \\
\hline
442 \cdot 08 \\
\hline
\end{array}
$$

EXAMPLE 10

Find $17\frac{1}{2}$ % of 2456.

$$1\% \text{ of } 2456 = 24{\cdot}56$$

$$17\frac{1}{2}\% \text{ of } 2456 = 17{\cdot}5 \times 24{\cdot}56$$

$$= 429{\cdot}80$$

$$
\begin{array}{r}
24{\cdot}56 \\
\times \quad 17{\cdot}5 \\
\hline
12280 \\
171920 \\
245600 \\
\hline
429{\cdot}800 \\
\hline
\end{array}
$$

Exercise 3.11   *(Answers are given on page 106.)*

1.   Find 1% of

    (a) 250   *(b)* 1900   *(c)* 16 200   *(d)* 78·50

2.   Using the results you found in question 1, find

    (a) 5% of £250   *(b)* 8% of 1900 people

    (c) 6% of £16 200   *(d)* 2% of 78·50

3.   Use the above method for finding percentages to answer this question.

    Colin sees the plot of land he bought three years ago increase in value by 15%. If he bought it for £15 000, what is it worth now?

FINDING PERCENTAGES BY CONVERTING TO A DECIMAL

There is another way of finding percentages using decimals.

To find a certain percentage of a number, first turn the percentage into a decimal, i.e., divide it by 100, and then multiply this decimal by the number.

Like this:

EXAMPLE 11

Find 65% of 180.

$$65\% = 65 \div 100$$
$$= 0{\cdot}65$$
$$65\% \text{ of } 180 = 0{\cdot}65 \times 180$$
$$= 117$$

```
        180
   ×   0·65
   ────────
        900
      10800
      00000
   ────────
     117·00
   ────────
```

EXAMPLE 12

Find $2\frac{1}{2}$ % of £3400.

$$2\tfrac{1}{2}\% = 2{\cdot}5 \div 100$$
$$= 0{\cdot}025$$
$$2\tfrac{1}{2}\% \text{ of } £3400 = £(0{\cdot}025 \times 3400)$$
$$= £85$$

```
        3400
   ×   0·025
   ─────────
       17000
       68000
       00000
   ─────────
      85·000
   ─────────
```

IN CONCLUSION . . .

This book has looked at only some of the methods of handling fractions, percentages and decimals. There are many ways of arriving at the correct answer.

One method of finding a particular percentage is worth noting as it is performed countless times in this country every day, usually by people using a calculator. It is finding VAT at $17\frac{1}{2}$%. Here's how to do it *without* using a calculator.

EXAMPLE 13

Find $17\frac{1}{2}$% of £550.

Step one:	Find 10% of £500	£50	(500 ÷ 10 = 50)
Step two:	Find 5% of £500	£25	(50 ÷ 2 = 25)
Step three:	Find $2\frac{1}{2}$% of £500	£12.50	(25 ÷ 2 = 12.5)
Step four:	Add up:	£87.50	

Easy isn't it? The method works because $17\frac{1}{2} = 10 + 5 + 2\frac{1}{2}$ *but let's hope the Chancellor doesn't change the rate of VAT!*

Wherever there are people dealing with numbers: accountants, clerks, salesmen, shopkeepers or tradesmen, there will be different ways of doing these sorts of calculation. All of them will have found their own ways to survive fractions, percentages and decimals and so can you.

SUMMARY

♦   Fractions, percentages and decimals are essentially the same thing and we can change easily from one to another

♦   To change a decimal to a percentage, multiply by one hundred, i.e., shift the decimal point two places to the right.

♦   To change a percentage to a decimal, divide by one hundred, i.e., shift the decimal point two places to the left.

♦   Finding one per cent of a number is the same as dividing that number by one hundred.

♦   Having found one per cent of a number, we can quickly find any other percentage of that number simply by multiplying.

♦   Percentages can also be found by first changing the percentage into a decimal and then multiplying.

ANSWERS

Exercise 3.10

1. *(a)* 0·28   *(b)* 0·4   *(c)* 0·04   *(d)* 0·975
2. *(a)* 14%   *(b)* 6%   *(c)* 3%   *(d)* 2·5%

Exercise 3.11

1. *(a)* 2·5   *(b)* 19   *(c)* 162   *(d)* 0·785
2. *(a)* £12.50   *(b)* 152 people   *(c)* £972   *(d)* £1.57
3. £17 250

Exercise 3.12

1. *(a)* 0·86   *(b)* 0·14   *(c)* 0·025   *(d)* 0·0125
2. *(a)* 36 120 people   *(b)* 3150 ha   *(c)* £10 000   *(d)* 62·5 kg
3. £262.50

TEST ON DECIMALS

1. What is the place value of 5 in

    (a) 527·9,

    (b) 0·025? **(2)**

2. *(a)* Multiply 0·025 by one hundred.

    (b) Divide 527·19 by 10. **(2)**

3. *(a)* Add 2·5 + 0·01 + 42·1 + 0·002.

    (b) Subtract 0·21 from 44·965. **(2)**

4. What is the area of a rectangular room 6·25 m long and 4·4 m wide? **(2)**

5. A packaging firm is designing a box to take a stack of books. The books are all 0·8 cm thick and the box must be 48 cm high.

    How many books will fit in the box? **(2)**

6. *(a)* What is 2·42 as a mixed number?

    (b) What is $\frac{3}{8}$ as a decimal? **(2)**

7. $\frac{3}{7} = 0.428571$ correct to six decimal places. Round it off to

    (a) one decimal place,

    (b) two decimal places,

    (c) three decimal places. **(3)**

8. What is $\frac{12}{25}$ as

    (a) a decimal?

    (b) a percentage? **(2)**

9. What is 0·02 as

    (a) a fraction?

    (b) a percentage? **(2)**

10. *(a)* What is 1% of 22 000?

   (b) Use your answer in *(a)* to find 6% of 22 000.

   (c) If Brian gets a pay rise of 6% on his old salary of £22 000, what is his new salary? **(3)**

11. *(a)* Express $5\frac{1}{2}$ % as a decimal.

   (b) Use your answer from *(a)* to find $5\frac{1}{2}$ % of 2200.

   (c) A tourist attraction sees visitor numbers drop by $5\frac{1}{2}$ % from last year. If there were 2200 visitors last year, how many visitors came this year? **(3)**

Total marks (25)

ANSWERS TO TEST ON DECIMALS

1. (a) One hundred.
    (b) One thousandth.   (2)

2. (a) 2·5
    (b) 52·719   (2)

3. (a) 44·612
    (b) 44·755   (2)

4. 27·5 square metres   (2)

5. 60 books   (2)

6. (a) $2\frac{42}{100} = 2\frac{21}{50}$
    (b) 0·375   (2)

7. (a) 0·4
    (b) 0·43
    (c) 0·429   (3)

8. (a) 0·48
    (b) 48%   (2)

9. (a) $\frac{2}{100} = \frac{1}{50}$
    (b) 2%   (2)

10. (a) 220
    (b) 1320
    (c) £23 320   (3)

11. (a) 0·055
    (b) 121
    (c) 2079   (3)

Total marks (25)

INTERPRETING YOUR TEST SCORE

Less than 12   You still have not understood the fundamentals of decimals and you need more help.

12 to 17   The basics are there but more practice is needed on the weak areas.

18 to 21   You have a good understanding of the subject which should see you through.

22+   Congratulations! You have mastered decimals.

MULTIPLICATION TABLES

2	**3**	**4**	**5**
1 × 2 = 2	1 × 3 = 3	1 × 4 = 4	1 × 5 = 5
2 × 2 = 4	2 × 3 = 6	2 × 4 = 8	2 × 5 = 10
3 × 2 = 6	3 × 3 = 9	3 × 4 = 12	3 × 5 = 15
4 × 2 = 8	4 × 3 = 12	4 × 4 = 16	4 × 5 = 20
5 × 2 = 10	5 × 3 = 15	5 × 4 = 20	5 × 5 = 25
6 × 2 = 12	6 × 3 = 18	6 × 4 = 24	6 × 5 = 30
7 × 2 = 14	7 × 3 = 21	7 × 4 = 28	7 × 5 = 35
8 × 2 = 16	8 × 3 = 24	8 × 4 = 32	8 × 5 = 40
9 × 2 = 18	9 × 3 = 27	9 × 4 = 36	9 × 5 = 45
10 × 2 = 20	10 × 3 = 30	10 × 4 = 40	10 × 5 = 50
11 × 2 = 22	11 × 3 = 33	11 × 4 = 44	11 × 5 = 55
12 × 2 = 24	12 × 3 = 36	12 × 4 = 48	12 × 5 = 60

6	**7**	**8**	**9**
1 × 6 = 6	1 × 7 = 7	1 × 8 = 8	1 × 9 = 9
2 × 6 = 12	2 × 7 = 14	2 × 8 = 16	2 × 9 = 18
3 × 6 = 18	3 × 7 = 21	3 × 8 = 24	3 × 9 = 27
4 × 6 = 24	4 × 7 = 28	4 × 8 = 32	4 × 9 = 36
5 × 6 = 30	5 × 7 = 35	5 × 8 = 40	5 × 9 = 45
6 × 6 = 36	6 × 7 = 42	6 × 8 = 48	6 × 9 = 54
7 × 6 = 42	7 × 7 = 49	7 × 8 = 56	7 × 9 = 63
8 × 6 = 48	8 × 7 = 56	8 × 8 = 64	8 × 9 = 72
9 × 6 = 54	9 × 7 = 63	9 × 8 = 72	9 × 9 = 81
10 × 6 = 60	10 × 7 = 70	10 × 8 = 80	10 × 9 = 90
11 × 6 = 66	11 × 7 = 77	11 × 8 = 88	11 × 9 = 99
12 × 6 = 72	12 × 7 = 84	12 × 8 = 96	12 × 9 = 108

10	**11**	**12**
1 × 10 = 10	1 × 11 = 11	1 × 12 = 12
2 × 10 = 20	2 × 11 = 22	2 × 12 = 24
3 × 10 = 30	3 × 11 = 33	3 × 12 = 36
4 × 10 = 40	4 × 11 = 44	4 × 12 = 48
5 × 10 = 50	5 × 11 = 55	5 × 12 = 60
6 × 10 = 60	6 × 11 = 66	6 × 12 = 72
7 × 10 = 70	7 × 11 = 77	7 × 12 = 84
8 × 10 = 80	8 × 11 = 88	8 × 12 = 96
9 × 10 = 90	9 × 11 = 99	9 × 12 = 108
10 × 10 = 100	10 × 11 = 110	10 × 12 = 120
11 × 10 = 110	11 × 11 = 121	11 × 12 = 132
12 × 10 = 120	12 × 11 = 132	12 × 12 = 144

MULTIPLICATION and DIVISION CHART

1	2	3	4	5	6	7	8	9	10	11	12
2	4	6	8	10	12	14	16	18	20	22	24
3	6	9	12	15	18	21	24	27	30	33	36
4	8	12	16	20	24	28	32	36	40	44	48
5	10	15	20	25	30	35	40	45	50	55	60
6	12	18	24	30	36	42	48	54	60	66	72
7	14	21	28	35	42	49	56	63	70	77	84
8	16	24	32	40	48	56	64	72	80	88	96
9	18	27	36	45	54	63	72	81	90	99	108
10	20	30	40	50	60	70	80	90	100	110	120
11	22	33	44	55	66	77	88	99	110	121	132
12	24	36	48	60	72	84	96	108	120	132	144

Printed by Bell & Bain, Ltd., Glasgow, Scotland, U.K.